FRUMPY the CLOWN
VOLUME ONE:
FREAKING OUT THE NEIGHBORS

WRITTEN AND ILLUSTRATED BY
JUDD WINICK

COVER COLORS BY
GUY MAJOR

BOOK DESIGN BY **STEVEN BIRCH @ SERVO**
EDITED BY **JAMES LUCAS JONES**
ASSISTANT EDITING BY **JAMIE S. RICH**

Published by Oni Press, Inc.
Joe Nozemack, publisher
Jamie S. Rich, editor in chief
James Lucas Jones, assistant editor/webmaster

*Frumpy the Clown was originally published and
syndicated in a daily format by Creator's Syndicate.
This book is published with their permission.*

ONI PRESS, INC.
6336 SE Milwaukie Avenue, PMB30
Portland, OR 97202
USA

www.onipress.com
www.frumpy.com

First edition: January 2001
ISBN 1-929998-11-2

1 3 5 7 9 10 8 6 4 2
PRINTED IN CANADA.

A very long and rambling
FOREWORD

It's around two in the afternoon here in San Francisco.

I'm listening to Tom Waits' *Mule Variations*, nursing a cup of tea (double strong – I may be a sissy who doesn't drink coffee but I do make the effort where I can), downloading the movie trailer to *Crouching Tiger, Hidden Dragon* and composing the very words you're reading. Multi-tasking in the non-productive kind of way.

I'm here to discuss *Frumpy the Clown*, origins and exits. If you are picking up this book, I'm assuming you have a modicum of interest in the subject. I've told this tale in bits and pieces over the years (y'know, like *three* years), but this is it from the beginning…

It all began with the comic strip *Garfield*. I loved *Garfield*. I was probably eleven and I thought *Garfield* was the funniest thing in the whole wide world. Garfield said "Big, fat hairy deal" and I just pissed myself. I have gone back and looked at my dog-eared copies of the first three *Garfield* collections and they kind of hold up. They are still funny. Most importantly for me at the time, as a kid who drew lots of pictures, lotsa cartoons, my vocation came into focus. I would be a nationally syndicated cartoonist. Yeah. I'd be one of *those* guys. I had decided by the year's end that I had accumulated enough skill in my work (my work consisting of a comic strip entitled *Lester*, about a disgruntled cat and his owner) that it was only a matter of time until I was scooped up by one of the major syndicates. I would, of course, finish elementary school to appease my parents. The offers did not pour in, so I figured I would just continue as I was. Heck, time was on my side.

When I was thirteen or so, my grandmother, Nana Dot, sent me an article from the Sunday magazine section of the *Miami Herald*. It was about local cartoonist Berke Breathed and his comic strip *Bloom County*. It had maybe six of his strips in the article. It was like lightning hitting. I would only realize later (later meaning *today*, actually) that no other artist has had greater impact on me than Berke Breathed. If I can put into one word what this comic strip did to me, it would be **incensed**. It made me WANT to be a cartoonist. It was hysterical, drawn expressively, loved the same crap I loved (what comic strip worshipped "Hill Street Blues" and referenced "M*A*S*H*"?), and it tackled issues. It was satire and I was relating to said satire before I even knew what that word meant.

I was inspired.

My choice in vocation hadn't changed, just my approach. I proceeded to rip-off *Bloom County* for the next several years. There were bursts of creative vision when I'd rip-off other cartoonists; I had a very eventful B. Kliban period, which honestly produced some of my most original work. But like the addict in recovery, I went back to my old tricks. I was attending the University of Michigan and got lucky enough to do a comic strip in the school's paper, *The Michigan Daily*. It was a daily strip called *Nuts and Bolts*. It had its fans and detractors from the beginning, as well as a character named Lumus who's stature, color scheme and attitude was similar to *Bloom County*'s **Opus** ("Lumus is not a penguin…" I would point out to whoever made it an issue). But something happened in my Junior year –

I got pretty good.

Beginning with a story line about Lumus getting dumped by his girlfriend, and then introducing a character named Frumpy the Clown –
    "… like Krusty the Clown from 'The Simpsons'…?" people would ask me.
    "Frumpy is not a penguin…" I would reply and then walk away quickly –

This was when it began to feel right. I felt like a real cartoonist. I was also conscious of the fact that I was getting better.

I graduated from college with a development contract from Universal Press Syndicate. They would drop me a year later. This is all laid out in my graphic novel, *Pedro and Me*. (That isn't a plug, it's just *told* better in the book). I tried other syndicates:
    "No, thank you."
Then I tried something drastic. Forget all this Gen-X political garbage, I'll give them what they want. A *family* comic strip. I moved Frumpy in with a modern American family.
    "No, thank you," said the syndicates.

I was broken.

I then appeared on 'The Real World' tried to figure out what kind of cartoonist I wanted to be, and had given up on the idea of syndication. How's that for concise. In 1995, I got a phone call from an office manager at Creator's Syndicate. Not an editor, just someone who worked there and had seen me on the show.

"Have you ever sent us your work?"

"Yeah, twice."

"Want to send us something new…?"

No, I thought, "I'll send you something old." I just mailed them my *Nuts and Bolts* submissions and my *Frumpy* submissions.

Two months later, my partner Pam and I were in Germany giving AIDS education lectures at high schools ("Vas Puck really like zat…?") and we were checking messages on our answering machine at home. I got one from Anita Tobias, chief editor at Creator's; they loved Frumpy and wanted to talk to me about syndication.

"WHAT TIME IS IT IN LOS ANGELES!?" I screamed.

In July of 1996, *Frumpy the Clown* debuted in about fifteen papers. I had attained my dream. This was the literal IT. I was happy. It didn't pay very well, I wasn't in that many papers, but I wasn't in it for the bucks. My freelance stuff kept me more than afloat, and my art, soul, and passions were fueled by the strip. *Too cool.*

Then something weird started to happen. I started losing my enthusiasm. While juggling my career as a cartoonist, I had spent several years prior to this comic strip touring the country doing AIDS education and lecturing about my "Real World" roommate and friend Pedro Zamora. Now that was over and the comic strip felt unfulfilling. It was never the kind of comic strip I wanted to do, and I didn't feel like I was saying anything. It felt thin.

I really agonized over what I was creating. Was this what I'm supposed to do? I decided to give something else a try. I had read and been a fan of comic books my whole life but I never thought it was the medium for me. I didn't have the chops or the real pull towards it. But the gravity somehow found me in a way of story telling and a subject. I began a graphic novel about Pedro. When I finished the first draft, I decided to quit the comic strip. Not just *Frumpy the Clown,* but comic strips as a medium.

In the end, it wasn't too much about *this* comic strip but it was about the story telling. In comic strips, you are only allotted a certain amount of space, movement and emotion. Many succeed: *Doonesbury, For Better or For Worse, Calvin and Hobbes, Luann, Funky Winkerbean,* and *Peanuts.* They all deliver a lot of emotional punch when they want to. I actually don't have the tools to do it in this format.

I wanted to tell stories. *Pedro and Me begat Road Trip.* Then quitting *Frumpy begat Barry Ween.* And from there I went on to hero books like *Green Lantern, X-Men* and a few others.

I was and am happy as a creator. And, thank God, people are reading and enjoying.

THE BIG WRAP UP.

So, now you have the collection of the comic strip that drove me away from comic strips.

I spent the last years thinking to myself, "That damned strip…good riddance."

I have to admit two things. One, people always seemed to like it. I got significantly more fan mail than hate mail on *Frumpy.* I hated letting people down when I quit. And two, in the process of putting this book together, I read over the entire run of *Frumpy the Clown.* Y'know what? It's good. In all due modesty, most of it is pretty goddamned funny. And for the first time I missed it. It's great having a soap box to climb onto, a place to vent on the most recent stirrings in popular culture, and an avenue to have jokes about cats burping. And I see some development of what is to come. Minus the potty mouth, Brad and Kim bear a resemblance to Barry Ween. And Frumpy is as cranky, softhearted and dangerous as the little guy will ever be. I also see all my commie issues creeping in and out. And there is mention of an Uncle Peter who would have turned out to be gay.

I love Frumpy. I do miss him. But I left with the comment that "I have other fish to fry."

Here's the last dance before the clambake. I hope you dig it.

Judd Winick
December, 2000
San Francisco.

Actually downloading the **Tomb Raider** *trailer but wanted to sound cool.*

MONA, YOU EVER SELL LEMONADE AS A KID?

SURE.

SO, YOU'D UNDERSTAND IF THE KIDS GOT THAT SAME ENTREPRENEURIAL SPIRIT, RIGHT?

YEAH. IT'D BE FUN.

SO, YOU'D UNDERSTAND IF THEY GOT A LITTLE OVERZEALOUS.

I SUPPOSE. I JUST— OH MY...

WHAT DID THEY— SOLD BOTH CARS.

THE CARS!?!

NOT VERY WELL, I MIGHT ADD. THEY SHOULD HAVE GOTTEN A LOT MORE FOR THE VOLVO.

SO, YOU KIDS MADE DINNER, HUH?

WE SURE DID!

PLAP PLAP

WELL, IT LOOKS, UM, INTERESTING ENOUGH. WHAT EXACTLY IS IT?

WE CALL IT "GREEN GOULASH SURPRISE."

IS THAT A FACT?

WHAT IS IT?

ALL THE PLAY-DOH IS MISSING, I'M EATING SALAD.

WHO WANTS MORE GRAVY!?

FRUMPY, I BROUGHT SOMETHING HOME FOR YOU FROM SCHOOL.

YEAH, WHAT IS IT?

HOO

SQUEEZE

Y'KNOW, YOU KIDS ARE TURNING ME INTO A REAL SAP.

SORRY.

'S OKAY.

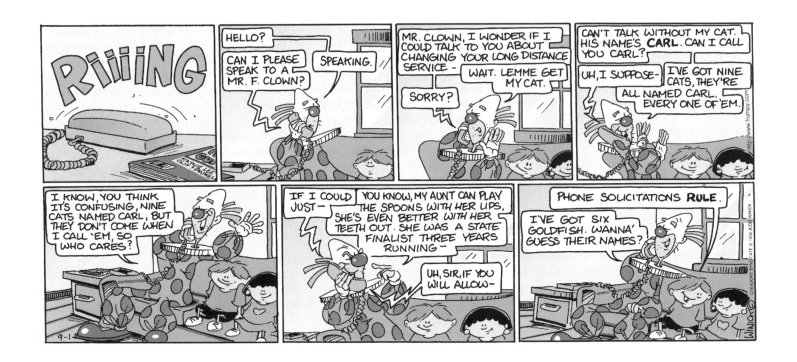

Row 1, Panel 1: MOMMY, AT SCHOOL, ZACH TAYLOR SAID THAT ANIMALS DON'T GO TO HEAVEN, AND IF THAT'S TRUE, THEN MY GOLDFISH **BOBO** WHO DIED DIDN'T GO TO HEAVEN AND I'LL NEVER SEE HIM AGAIN.

Row 1, Panel 2: IS THAT TRUE?
UH...

Row 1, Panel 3: UM, WELL... I, UH, HMMN. WELL, BOBO, UM, WELL...

Row 1, Panel 4: YOU WERE RIGHT. SHE WAS SPUTTERING LIKE BAD PLUMBING.
TOMORROW, ASK HER WHERE BABIES COME FROM.

WINICK © CREATORS SYNDICATE © 1996 JUDD WINICK 9/13
http://www.frumpy.com

Row 2, Panel 1: DO YOU THINK WE'RE BORING?
US? NO. WHY?
I FEEL LIKE WE'RE...MUNDANE.
MUNDANE?

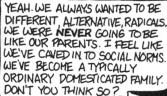

Row 2, Panel 2: YEAH. WE ALWAYS WANTED TO BE DIFFERENT, ALTERNATIVE, RADICALS. WE WERE **NEVER** GOING TO BE LIKE OUR PARENTS. I FEEL LIKE WE'VE CAVED IN TO SOCIAL NORMS. WE'VE BECOME A TYPICALLY ORDINARY DOMESTICATED FAMILY. DON'T YOU THINK SO?

http://www.frumpy.com

Row 2, Panel 3: MY baby takes the morning train, he works from 9 to 5 and then... HEY, CAMPERS! BATH TIME!
...he takes another home again to find me waitin' for him...
Y.M.C.A.

Row 2, Panel 4: NAH. PEOPLE THINK WE'RE FREAKIN' NUTS.
I GUESS SO.
HEY! WHERE'S THE LOOFAH SPONGE!?

WINICK © 9/14 CREATORS SYNDICATE © 1996 JUDD WINICK

Row 3, Panel 1: MY PARENTS ARE BOZOS!
REALLY?

Row 3, Panel 2: I'M PUNISHED. GROUNDED A WEEK OVER NOTHING.
THAT SO.

Row 3, Panel 3: THEY'RE ALWAYS GROUNDING ME FOR THE STUPIDEST THINGS.

WINICK © 7-29 http://www.frumpy.com
CREATORS SYNDICATE © 1996 JUDD WINICK

Row 3, Panel 4: I HEARD YOU TRIED TO FLUSH A GRAPEFRUIT DOWN THE TOILET.
EXACTLY. THEY HAVE NO RESPECT FOR SCIENCE.

SO. YOU TWO GOT INTO A FIGHT AT RECESS?

YEAH.

UH-HUH.

WHAT HAPPENED?

WELL, JASON RAN INTO ME, SO I GAVE HIM A NOOGIE.

WHAT DID I SAY ABOUT VIOLENCE?

WELL, YEAH, WE KNOW, BUT, UH, WELL, THE CLASS TOOK A VOTE LAST WEEK, AND WE COLLECTIVELY DECIDED TO ALLOW NOOGIES.

WHAT?!

WELL, GEEZ, FRUMPY, Y'GOTTA GIVE US AN OUTLET.

SERIOUSLY, THIS IS SO CONFINING.

PURPLE NURPLES ARE OK, TOO!

MR. CLOWN?

PRUMPY.

PRUMPY, I WANTED TO SPEAK TO YOU ABOUT THE BOOK REPORTS YOUR CLASS HAS BEEN DOING THIS WEEK.

YEAH?

WELL, I'VE HEARD THE CHILDREN HAVE BEEN GETTING A BIT OVERZEALOUS IN THEIR PRESENTATIONS.

I'M NOT ONE TO STIFLE CREATIVITY.

I'M NOT EITHER...

IT'S JUST THAT A CERTAIN AMOUNT OF RESTRAINT AND DECORUM IS REQUIRED IN A CLASSROOM.

WELL, WE'RE WELL WITHIN THOSE BOUNDS, I ASSURE YOU.

HONESTLY?

OH, YEAH.

"THE LORD OF THE FLIES," BY WILLIAM GOLDING.

THE BOOK I READ IS CALLED "CHARLIE AND THE CHOCOLATE FACTORY."

Y'KNOW, IT'S DIFFERENT FROM THE MOVIE.

WHAT?

THE MOVIE "WILLY WONKA AND THE CHOCOLATE FACTORY" IS DIFFERENT FROM THAT BOOK IT WAS BASED ON.

DID I SNAG YOU?

OH, BIG TIME.

NICE TRY.

I WISH. I'M GONNA KILL THAT GUY AT BLOCKBUSTER.

33

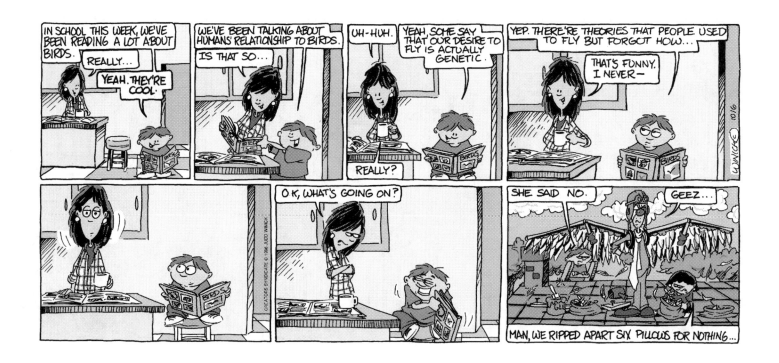

FRUMPY, MY PARENTS WON'T LET ME GO ON THE MUSEUM FIELD TRIP.

WHY?

I'M BEING OPPRESSED! THEY'RE TRYING TO CENSOR MY ARTISTIC APPRECIATION. **THEY** THINK I CAN'T HANDLE THE EXPLICIT NATURE OF SOME OF THE EXHIBITS...

THAT'S WHAT THEY SAID?

NO, BUT THAT'S THE TRUTH.

THEY SAID I'M GROUNDED BECAUSE I SHAVED MY SISTER'S HEAD.

BUT THEY CAN'T FOOL YOU.

HECK NO. IT DIDN'T WORK WHEN I BURNED DOWN THE GARAGE, AND IT WON'T WORK NOW...

10/22

AND HERE WE HAVE ANOTHER GREEK SCULPTURE...

EEUWW...

OH, C'MON, SCOTT, THIS IS ART.

IT'S GROSS.

NUDITY ISN'T SOMETHING THAT SHOULD BE CONSIDERED REPULSIVE.

NO, NO, NAKED I CAN HANDLE.

I JUST CAN'T GET OVER HOW **FAT** THIS GAL IS.

A STEP AEROBICS CLASS WOULD NOT HAVE **KILLED** THIS WOMAN.

10/23

I SEE YOU FOUND VAN GOGH.

YEAH, I LIKE IT.

YOU KNOW, HE NEVER SOLD A PAINTING WHEN HE WAS ALIVE.

REALLY? I THOUGHT HE WAS SUPPOSED TO BE **GOOD**...

ANDREW, JUST BECAUSE SOMETHING SELLS, IT DOESN'T MEAN IT'S GOOD.

LIKE "BAYWATCH."

YEAH.

10/24

47

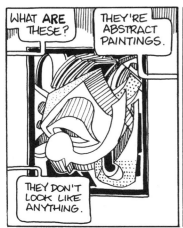

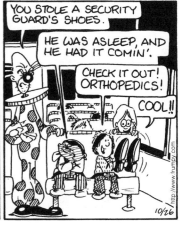

Row 1:

Panel 1: PRUMPY, WHAT'S WRONG WITH A TRADITIONAL THANKSGIVING PLAY?
THANKSGIVING PLAY AUDITIONS →
FRUMPY T. CLOWN DIRECTOR

Panel 2: EVERYTHING'S WRONG WITH IT. IT'S BIASED AND HISTORICALLY INACCURATE.

Panel 3: SO, WHAT ARE YOU GOING TO DO INSTEAD OF HAPPY TURKEYS, PILGRIMS, AND INDIANS?

Panel 4: SINGING VEGETABLES, GREEDY PILGRIMS, AND A **WHOLE** LOT OF DISGRUNTLED NATIVE AMERICANS.
WONDERFUL. "OLIVER STONE'S THANKSGIVING."
11/26

Row 2:

Panel 1: I'LL TELL THEE. LIFE AND DEATH! I AM ASHAM'D...
THANKSGIVING PLAY AUDITIONS →
FRUMPY T. CLOWN, DIRECTOR

Panel 2: THAT THOU HAST POWER TO SHAKE MY MANHOOD THUS,
KING LEAR BY WILLIAM SHAKESPEAR

Panel 3: BLAST AND FOGS UPON THEE!! PIERCE EVERY SENSE ABOUT THEE! OLD, FOND EYES, I'LL PLUCK YE **OUT**!

Panel 4: DID I GET IT?
KID, YOU'RE OUR LEAD PUMPKIN...
THANK YOU.
11/27

Row 3:

Panel 1: THIS THANKSGIVING PLAY IS COMPLETELY OUT OF HAND...
HOW, PRINCIPAL CARR?
DIRECTOR

Panel 2: THE CHILDREN ARE TAKING THIS ALL WAY TOO SERIOUSLY. YOU'VE GOT THEM ALL WORKED UP.
I HAVE NOT.

Panel 3: THEY ARE MERELY GETTING INTO THE THEATER EXPERIENCE.
OH, REALLY.

Panel 4: WHAT'S MY MOTIVATION?
YOU'RE A SQUASH!!
I CAN'T WORK WITH THIS.
11/28

WELCOME TO OUR THANKSGIVING DAY SALUTE.

LONG AGO THE NATIVE AMERICANS ROAMED THIS LAND. THEY LIVED AND THRIVED.

THEN CAME THE WHITE SETTLERS WHO TOOK ALL WE HAD AND LEFT THE PLAINS STAINED WITH THE BLOOD OF HUNDREDS OF THOUSANDS!

11/29

I LIKED IT BETTER LAST YEAR WHEN THE INDIANS SANG "BORN IN THE U.S.A."

CONGRATS, MR. DIRECTOR.

THANKS, GUYS.

I'VE NEVER SEEN THE THANKSGIVING STORY TOLD QUITE LIKE THAT.

NO HARVEST, NO TURKEY, NO FEAST, JUST BRUTAL DESCRIPTIONS OF THE PERSECUTION OF NATIVE AMERICANS.

SO, YOU ENJOYED IT?

NOT AT ALL. WE'RE RACKED WITH GUILT.

WELL, YOU'VE EARNED IT.

HEY, THANKS.

11/30

WOW, LOOK, NEW STAR WARS ACTION FIGURES ON THE HOME SHOPPING CHANNEL.

LET'S ORDER 'EM!!

HI. WE WANTED TO ORDER—NO, WE DON'T HAVE A CREDIT CARD... CASH ON DELIVERY? I GUESS SO...

WHO? MY DAD? YEAH, MY DAD WILL PAY FOR THE MERCHANDISE WHEN IT ARRIVES.

12/2

WE'VE GOT A LIVE ONE!!

IT'S TIMES LIKE THIS THAT I WISH WE WORKED ON COMMISSION.

HOME S

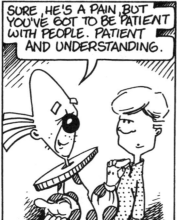

Panel 1: DO THE KIDS ALWAYS GET THIS EXCITED ABOUT MOVIES? / SORT OF, BUT THIS IS **THE EMPIRE STRIKES BACK**.

Panel 2: THE HYPE HAS GOT THEM ALL FIRED UP. THEY'D GO SEE IT EVERY DAY IF WE'D LET THEM. THEY'RE CRAZED.

Panel 3: I THINK YOU'RE EXAGGERATING. / REALLY? / YEAH, WHERE ARE THEY?

Panel 4: THEY'VE BEEN WAITING IN THE CAR FOR 20 MINUTES. STOP THAT HONKING, WE'RE COMIN'!!

2/25

Panel 1: WILL YOU HURRY UP, THE MOVIE'S GOING TO START. / WE HAVE TO WAIT FOR PRUMPY. / SHOWIN / RIKES BACK / MEN

Panel 2: HE SAID HE PAID TO SEE **THE EMPIRE STRIKES BACK** 17 YEARS AGO AND HE WASN'T GONNA PAY AGAIN. / SO, WHY ARE WE IN THE MEN'S ROOM?

Panel 3: CLACK

Panel 4: THIEF. / WHATEVER. WHO'S GOT MY TICKET STUB?

2/26

Panel 1: CAN I HAVE A SMALL POPCORN AND SODA? / YOU CAN GET A MEDIUM FOR 10¢ MORE. / THE EMPIRE STRIKES

Panel 2: WELL, OK... / OR A LARGE FOR 15¢ MORE? / I GUESS.

Panel 3: HOW 'BOUT AN EXTRA LARGE FOR 20¢ MORE? OR DOUBLE XXL FOR 25¢ MORE?

Panel 4: DON'T ASK. I JUST GOT SWEPT UP IN IT ALL. / POP CORN

2/27

Panel 1: HOW DO YOU GET GRAPE JUICE OUT OF WHITE CARPET? / TONIC WATER.

Panel 2: DON'T YOU WANNA SEE WHAT THAT'S ABOUT? / NOT YET.

Panel 4: COULD I HAVE THE BIG SCISSORS? / NOW, WE GO. / GOTCHA.

3/7

Panel 1: SCOTT'S MOM WOULDN'T LET US WATCH "RAIDER'S OF THE LOST ARK." / WHY? IT'S THE EDITED FOR T.V. VERSION RIGHT?

Panel 2: IT HAD ONE OF THOSE PG T.V. RATINGS. SHE SAID WE COULDN'T WATCH IT ALONE AND SHE WAS TOO BUSY.

Panel 3: FIRST, THEY MADE RATINGS 'CAUSE PARENTS DON'T HAVE TIME TO SCREEN OUR SHOWS. THEN PARENTS WON'T WATCH THE SHOWS WE NEED GUIDANCE WITH.

Panel 4: INDY, THROW ME THE IDOL, I'LL THROW YOU THE WHIP!

3/8

Panel 1: WHEN I GROW UP, I WANT TO BE AN ATTORNEY. / WHEN I GROW UP REPORTS.

Panel 2: AND WHEN IT IS SAID, "GROW UP." IT IS TO MEAN FROM 25-30 YEARS OF AGE. ADDITIONAL YEARS CAN BE ADDED IF AGREED UPON BY BOTH PARTIES.

Panel 3: AND "WANT" IS IN NO WAY A GUARANTEE THAT SAID PERSON, BEING "I," IS — / WHOA. JUST HOW LONG IS THIS?

Panel 4: SIXTY PAGES. NOT INCLUDING THE ADDENDUM. / WILL YOU SIT DOWN NOW IF I GIVE YOU AN A? / I'LL NEED IT IN WRITING.

3/10

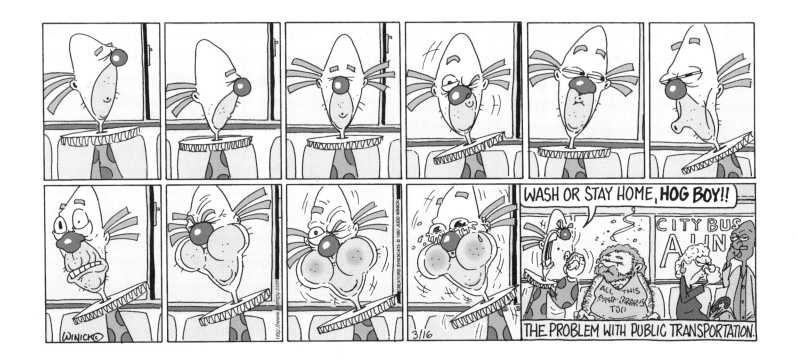

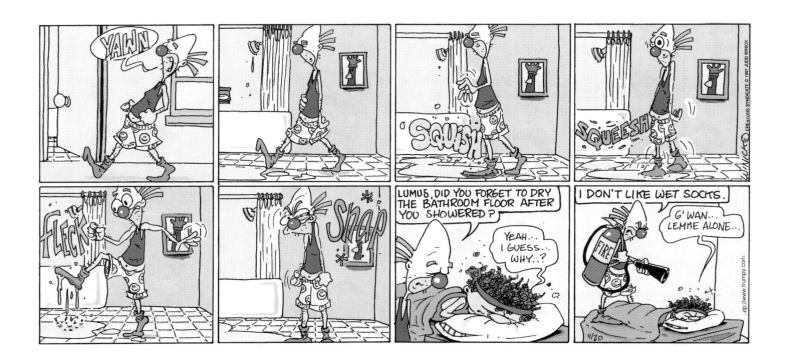

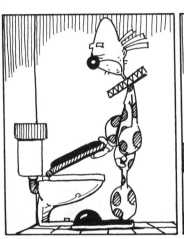

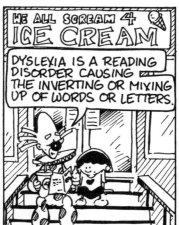

Panel 1: FRUMPY'S ON HIS WAY TO THE HOSPITAL! / WHAT?

Panel 2: HE WAS SPRAYING FAKE BLOOD ON PEOPLE WEARING FUR COATS. SOMEBODY CLOCKED HIM ONE. HARD. / SPORTS

Panel 3: IS HE OK? / I DON'T KNOW. THEY SAID HE'S PRETTY DISORIENTED. / 5/9

Panel 4: AM I THE ONLY ONE WHO THOUGHT "THE ENGLISH PATIENT" WAS SLOW? IS IT ME? / ANOTHER 10 MG'S OF VALIUM FOR BOZO. / CREATORS SYNDICATE © 1997 JUDD WINICK

Panel 1: YOU CAN TAKE HIM HOME. HE'S GOT A MILD CONCUSSION, SO TAKE IT EASY. / THANKS, DOCTOR.

Panel 2: I CAN'T BELIEVE YOU SPRAYED FAKE BLOOD ON PEOPLE. YOU WERE ASKING FOR IT. / EXIT

Panel 3: IF PEOPLE WEAR ANIMAL FUR, THEY CAN EXPECT ME TO STOP THEM! / http://www.frumpy.com

Panel 4: EXCEPT OLD LADIES WITH UMBRELLAS. I HAD HER ON THE ROPES 'TIL SHE CLUBBED ME WITH HER WALKER. GOOD THING I HAD MACE. / CREATORS SYNDICATE © 1997 JUDD WINICK / 5/10

Panel 1: WHY DO YOU HAVE TO TAKE YOUR DRIVER'S TEST AGAIN, MOM? / THEY SAY MY LICENSE EXPIRED.

Panel 2: I'VE BEEN DRIVING FOR FORTY YEARS! I LET IT LAPSE A LITTLE AND HAVE TO RETAKE MY TEST?

Panel 3: THEY WERE SO UPPITY ABOUT IT AT THE DMV. / IT DOES SEEM A BIT EXTREME. WHEN DID IT EXPIRE— / CREATORS SYNDICATE © 1997 JUDD WINICK

Panel 4: 1978!? / THAT'S WHAT I SAID! '78. BIG DEAL. I'VE BEEN BUSY. / http://www.frumpy.com / 5/12

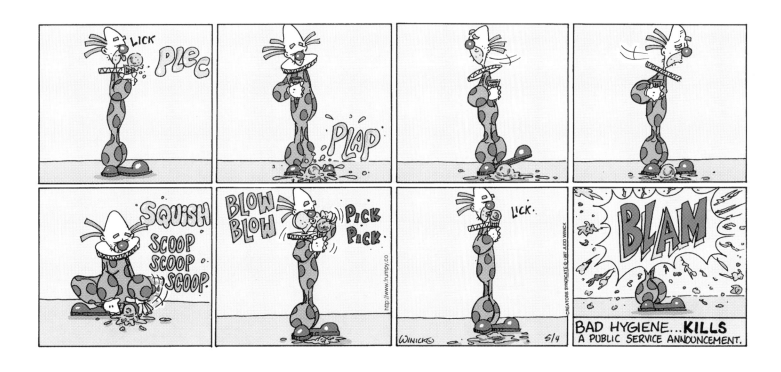

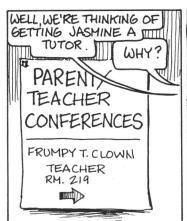

WELL, WE'RE THINKING OF GETTING JASMINE A TUTOR.

WHY?

PARENT/ TEACHER CONFERENCES

FRUMPY T. CLOWN TEACHER RM. 219 ➡

HER SCIENCE AND MATH SKILLS AREN'T WHERE THEY SHOULD BE.

WE'RE CONCERNED THAT SHE ISN'T ON THE ROAD TO AN IVY LEAGUE SCHOOL.

SHE'S NINE.

Y'SEE, HE THINKS WE STARTED LATE, TOO! WE DID THE PRENATAL FRENCH TAPES!

5/27 WINICK©

MARK'S DOING REAL WELL—

IS HE GONNA PLAY FOOTBALL?

PARENT/ TEACHER CONFERENCES

FRUMPY T. CLOWN TEACHER RM. 219 ➡

FOOTBALL. WELL, I'M JUST HIS—

HE'S SLOW, HE CAN'T THROW A BALL WORTH A SPIT.

I TEACH—

WE TRIED SOCCER, BASEBALL, FOOTBALL'S MY **LAST** SHOT!!

THIS EXPLAIN'S MARK'S TWITCH.

Y'GOTTA HELP ME, MAN, THE WIFE'S TALKING BALLET!

5/28 WINICK©

IT'S GOOD TO MEET YOU, MRS. CONNOR, I—

NO PROBLEM, NO PROBLEM.

PARENT/ TEACHER CONFERENCES

FRUMPY T. CLOWN TEACHER RM. 219 ➡

CAN WE KEEP THIS SHORT. I'VE GOT A 10 O'CLOCK I CAN'T MISS.

SURE. MY CONCERN IS THAT CHAD HAS BEEN ACTING OUT.

ACTING OUT, UH-HUH, UH-HUH (I need the Boston file) WHY WOULD HE DO THAT? (and New York.)

I DUNNO. LACK OF ATTENTION.

WAIT, LEMME CHECK WITH THE NANNY. CONSUELA? HOW'S CHAD BEEN?

BIEN, SENORA!

5/29 WINICK©

YOU'RE BEING EXTRADITED FOR A TRIAL IN OHIO?

WELL, I'VE JUST GOTTA PAY FOR SOME PARKING TICKETS...

CLICK

C'MON. THEY FILED FOR EXTRADITION FOR PARKING TICKETS? HOW MUCH COULD YOU OWE?

$4,300.

WHAT?

I'M NOT A PATIENT MAN AND THEY'VE GOT A LOT OF RED ZONES IN CLEVELAND, OK?

6/3

DEPARTING FLIGHTS
GATES 10 - 24 →
GATES 24 - 40 ↑

YEAH, FRUMPY PAID HIS PARKING TICKETS. WE'RE ON OUR WAY HOME.

IT WAS A $4,300 FINE... NO, HE'S IN A REAL BAD MOOD TO BOOT...

IT ALSO TOOK HIM OVER HALF AN HOUR TO FIND A SMOKING SECTION HERE AT THE AIRPORT...

YOU'RE REALLY NOT SUPPOSED TO BE HERE!!

HEY, GO PARK A PLANE, OK?

6/4

NUMENTAL AIRLIN

WE'RE BUMPED OFF OUR FLIGHT? WE'VE GOT TICKETS RIGHT HERE -

WE'RE OVERBOOKED.

WHY DO YOU DO THAT? WHY CONSTANTLY SELL MORE TICKETS THAN YOU HAVE SEATS?

I DON'T KNOW, SIR, I -

YOU NEVER KNOW! Y'KNOW WHY!? 'CAUSE YOUR AIRLINE STINKS! YER A BUNCH OF INCOMPETENT SHEEP WHO COULDN'T EFFECTIVELY RUN A "DENNY'S"!! THAT'S WHY!!

SECURITY

SMART.

OBVIOUS RACISM.

YOU MOONED HIM.

SHUT-UP.

6/5

WE'RE FINE, BUT THE KIDS ARE GOING NUTS...

WITH SCHOOL OVER AND **BATMAN AND ROBIN** COMING OUT ON FRIDAY, THEY'RE CRAZED.

I THINK WE'LL ALL BE HAPPIER AFTER THE HYPE DIES DOWN...

GET ME DOWN **NOW!**

MORE LIKE **UP**, JOKER, UP THE RIVER...

CAN WE PLEASE CAMP OUT FOR **BATMAN AND ROBIN** TICKETS?

ON THE SIDEWALK ALL NIGHT? **NO.** THAT'S ONLY FOR GROWN UPS.

HOW WOULD YOU KNOW?

BECAUSE I DID IT A LOT, **AFTER** I TURNED SIXTEEN.

I MUST'VE CAMPED OUT FOR DOZENS OF CONCERTS. I'M A PRO. I - WAIT A MINUTE-

WHY DID I HAVE TO COME?

BECAUSE THEY WEREN'T THIS SMART BEFORE YOU SHOWED UP.

BATMAN · and · ROBIN

○·○·○·○·○·○·○○

HERE I AM AGAIN. CAMPING OUT TO SEE A **BATMAN** MOVIE.

I'VE SEEN THE FIRST THREE MOVIES TWENTY TIMES EACH.

I'M GONNA SEE **THIS** ONE TWENTY TIMES, MAKING IT AN EVEN HUNDRED. IT'S ZEN, Y'KNOW?

I ASSUME I'M NOT THE FIRST TO TELL YOU TO "GET A LIFE"...

HECK NO. MY DAD DOES **ALL** THE TIME.

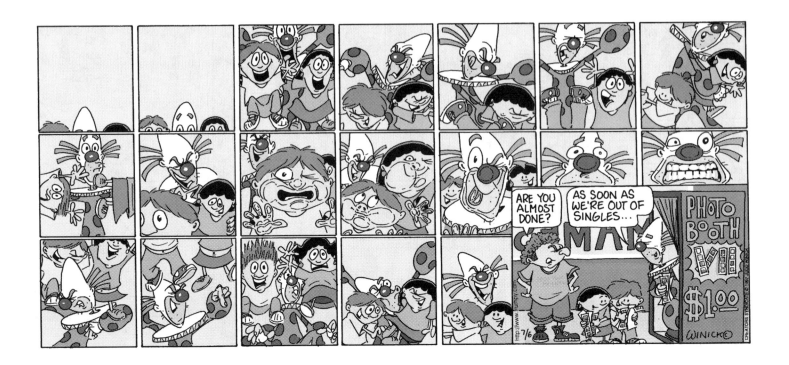

This page: *Frumpy The Clown* strip from *Oni Double Feature #3.*

These pages: Title cards done for the *Frumpy* Sunday strips.

This page: Early adventures of Frumpy in *Nuts & Bolts*.